English BASICS

FOR AGES 7 - 8 KEY STAGE 2

C000160892

Contents

Look and learn

A **prefix** is a group of letters we put **in front** of a word. Prefixes **change the meaning** of the word.

happy

unhappy

agree

disagree

Practice

Add the prefixes. Make some new words.

un

_un_ do   ____fair   ___dress   ____well   ___pack

1. _undo_   2. _____   3. _____   4. _____   5. _____

dis

_____trust   _____obey   _____honest   _____arm   ___place

6. _____   7. _____   8. _____   9. _____   10. _____

Challenge

1. Write the word that means the opposite of:

a) pack____unpack____   b) obey_____

c) fair   _____   d) dress   _____

e) trust   _____   f) honest _____

g) do   _____   h) arm   _____

i) place   _____   j) well   _____

2. Choose **un** or **dis** to complete each word.

a) _____bolt   b) _____own   c) _____charge

d) _____buckle   e) _____may   f) _____order

g) _____fasten   h) _____wrap   i) _____able

Verbs

Look and learn

A **verb** tells us what someone **is doing** or what **is happening**.

Emma **is digging** the garden.

Practice

Choose the best verb to complete each sentence.

| roared | broke | dived | took | fell |
| shone | stole | painted | knocked | bit |

1. The burglar _____stole_____ the money.

2. The boy _____ into the water.

3. Some lions _____ loudly.

4. Someone _____ on the front door.

5. The stone _____ the window.

6. Who _____ my apple?

7. Anna _____ a lovely picture.

8. Humpty Dumpty _____ off the wall.

9. The sun _____ in the sky.

10. The rocket _____ off for the moon.

Challenge

Match up the pairs of verbs with similar meanings.

vanish   push   speak   run   close   brush   moan   drink   draw   bang

talk   shut   sweep   disappear   hit   sketch   groan   race   shove   swallow

Look and learn

A **phoneme** is the **smallest unit of sound** in a word.
A phoneme may be made up of **one or more letters** which make **one sound**.

thr**ee** s**ea**ts

Practice

Circle the odd word out in each set.

1. seed   cheek   (poor)   meet

2. cool   now   soon   food

3. pay   car   barn   park

4. day   say   barn   way

5. seat   goat   beak   heap

6. goat   moan   road   pain

7. again   boy   annoy   destroy

8. crow   paw   flow   show

9. shout   mouse   sauce   south

10. coin   boil   voice   raw

Challenge

Choose the correct phoneme to complete each word.

1. b__ir__d	**oo ir**	**2.** p_____l	**ow oo**	**3.** r_____st	**oa ow**
4. p_____nt	**au ai**	**5.** cr_____n	**ay ow**	**6.** cr_____on	**ai ay**
7. ab_____t	**ow ou**	**8.** sp_____l	**oi ai**	**9.** b_____st	**ee ea**
10. bl_____	**ue oo**	**11.** gr_____	**aw ow**	**12.** b_____n	**ir ur**

le words

Look and learn

There are lots of words that end in **le**.

table   bottle   candle   apple

Practice

Sort these words into sets.

handle	table	twinkle	simple
people	ankle	needle	stumble
cable	sparkle	cradle	steeple

ble	dle	ple	kle

Challenge

Find and write the ten **le** words in the wordsearch puzzle.

a	b	j	u	n	g	l	e	d	e
u	n	c	l	e	f	g	h	k	m
o	p	q	r	c	i	r	c	l	e
s	t	e	a	g	l	e	v	w	x
y	z	a	b	s	i	n	g	l	e
z	a	n	k	l	e	p	e	f	g
h	i	j	b	u	b	b	l	e	k
d	a	z	z	l	e	m	o	p	q
r	s	n	i	b	b	l	e	t	u
v	w	x	y	c	a	t	t	l	e

1. jungle _____   2. _____

3. _____   4. _____

5. _____   6. _____

7. _____   8. _____

9. _____   10. _____

5

Punctuation marks

Look and learn

Punctuation marks make writing **easier to read** and **understand**.

This is a sheep.

Is this a cow?

What a lovely cat!

Most sentences end with a **full stop**.

If it is a **question**, a **question mark** is needed.

We put an **exclamation mark** when we **feel strongly** about something.

Practice

Rewrite these sentences. Put in the missing capital letters, full stops and question marks.

1. what colour is grass

_____

2. we have got curry for dinner

_____

3. my pencil is blunt

_____

4. where have you put my glasses

_____

5. when is your birthday

_____

6. the clock is broken

_____

Challenge

Write if each sentence is a question (Q) or an exclamation (E). Put in the missing question mark or exclamation mark.

1. Do you like sweets? (_Q_)

2. This is awful   (__)

3. Help, I'm drowning   (__)

4. Have you seen Sita   (__)

5. Who is the winner   (__)

6. Are you lost   (__)

7. Don't shout   (__)

8. When are you leaving   (__)

9. How much does it cost   (__)

10. Look out   (__)

11. Run for it   (__)

12. What time is it   (__)

Speech marks

Look and learn

When we write down what people say we use **speech marks**.
The **words a person says** go **inside** the speech marks.

How far is it to London?

It's about 20 miles.

"How far is it to London?" Mr Jones asked.   "It's about 20 miles," Emma replied.

Practice

Fill in the missing speech marks.

1. What would you like to eat? Mrs Jones asked.

2. I would like a sandwich, please, Tom replied.

3. What would you like in it? Mrs Jones asked.

4. Cheese and pickle, please, Tom answered.

5. I'll go and make it, Mrs Jones told Tom.

6. Shall I make us a cup of tea? Tom asked.

7. That would be nice, Mrs Jones replied.

8. Afterwards I'll watch TV, Tom added.

Challenge

Write something you think each person might say.

1. The doctor said, " _____ "

2. The police officer said, " _____ "

3. The footballer said, " _____ "

4. The astronaut said, " _____ "

5. The motorist said, " _____ "

6. The hairdresser said, " _____ "

7. The farmer said, " _____ "

8. The monster said, " _____ "

Look and learn

Many books are arranged in **alphabetical order**.

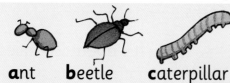

ant   **b**eetle   **c**aterpillar

s**n**ail   s**p**ider   s**q**uirrel

These words are arranged in alphabetical order according to their **first** letter.

These words are arranged in alphabetical order according to their **second** letter.

Practice

Write these words in order according to their first letter.

1. goat duck fish	**2.** teapot roof stall
_____	_____
3. lolly onion milk	**4.** car lorry ambulance
_____	_____

Write these words in order according to their second letter.

5. fog frog fly fall	**6.** shine skin spleen slip
_____	_____

Challenge

Think of a person's name beginning with each letter of the alphabet.

A _____	B _____	C _____	D _____	E _____
F _____	G _____	H _____	I _____	J _____
K _____	L _____	M _____	N _____	O _____
P _____	Q _____	R _____	S _____	T _____
U _____	V _____	W _____	X _____	Y _____	Z _____

Verbs – past tense

Look and learn

I **am planting** some seeds.

This is happening **now** so the verb is in the **present tense**.

Yesterday I **cut** the grass.

This happened in the **past** so the verb is in the **past tense**.

Practice

Match up each verb with its past tense.

1.	skip	carried	_____
2.	walk	saw	_____
3.	carry	went	_____
4.	tug	came	_____
5.	catch	tugged	_____
6.	see	skipped ⟶	skip skipped
7.	write	felt	_____
8.	come	caught	_____
9.	feel	wrote	_____
10.	go	walked	_____

Challenge

Choose the correct form of the verb to complete each sentence.

1. The boy _____ the apple.   (bit/bited)

2. I _____ myself when I fell over.   (hurt/hurted)

3. The ball _____ the window.   (breaked/broke)

4. I _____ the ball easily.   (catched/caught)

5. The jet _____ very fast.   (flied/flew)

6. I _____ with fear.   (shook/shaked)

7. My uncle _____ me a present.   (buyed/bought)

8. Who _____ this house?   (built/builded)

9. We _____ the sun rise.   (seed/saw)

10. The sunflower _____ very tall.   (growed/grew)

Commas

Look and learn

We use commas to **separate items on a list**. We do **not** usually put a comma before the word **and**.

In the fruit bowl there are apples, pears, bananas and oranges.

Practice

Put in the missing commas.

1. On the table were some potatoes carrots a cabbage and peas.

2. My favourite colours are red yellow blue and green.

3. In my bag I had some pens pencils crayons and a ruler.

4. Curry pizza burgers and sausages are my favourite foods.

5. The four seasons are summer autumn winter and spring.

6. The four pets I have are a dog a cat a gerbil and a mouse.

7. I collect stamps coins badges and shells.

8. History art maths and science are good subjects.

Challenge

Complete these lists. Remember the commas!

1. Four of my friends are _____

2. Four meals I hate are _____

3. Five presents I would like are _____

4. The days of the week are _____

_____

5. My three favourite subjects are _____

6. Four things in the fridge are _____

7. Out of the window I can see _____

8. In my bedroom I have _____

Words inside words

Look and learn

If you look closely, you can often see **small words** 'hiding' **inside longer words**.

be
cause
us
use

Practice

Find two small words hiding in each word.

main word	smaller words
1. tape	tap ape
2. many	
3. some	
4. every	
5. where	
6. heard	
7. before	
8. message	
9. shallow	
10. scare	

Challenge

Work out the words you are left with.

1. sl**owl**y – owl = _sly_

2. feared – ear = _____

3. money – one = _____

4. capable – able = _____

5. practice – act = _____

6. snowing – no = _____

7. father – her = _____

8. starting – art = _____

9. shallow – all = _____

10. carpet – pet = _____

Nouns

Look and learn

A **noun** is a **naming word**. It can be the name of a **person**, **place** or **thing**.

a car   a lady   a garage

Practice

Match up each noun with its definition.

1. A dentist	is used to separate two pieces of land.
2. A plumber	is a place where people worship.
3. A clown	is used to put letters in.
4. A church	helps us to look after our teeth.
5. A farm	is used to dig holes.
6. A shop	is a place where crops can be grown.
7. A fence	is used to cook food in.
8. A spade	mends burst water pipes.
9. An envelope	is a place where we buy things.
10. A saucepan	makes us laugh.

Challenge

Circle the odd noun out in each set. Explain your answer.

1.	cat dog (bus) mouse	All the others are animals.
2.	shoe apple banana orange	
3.	cabbage carrot potato trumpet	
4.	chair pencil table bed	
5.	knife fork book spoon	
6.	teacher doctor bear plumber	
7.	ball guitar drums piano	
8.	hammer window drill saw	

Singular and plural

Look and learn

A noun may be **singular** (when there is **only one** thing).
Nouns may be **plural** (when there is **more than one** thing).

singular	plural	singular	plural	singular	plural
one pen	lots of pens	one glass	lots of glasses	one fly	lots of flies

Practice

Complete the chart.

	singular	plural
1.	one car	lots of _____
2.	one _____	lots of books
3.	one brush	lots of _____
4.	one _____	lots of buses
5.	one dish	lots of _____
6.	one fox	lots of _____
7.	one baby	lots of _____
8.	one _____	lots of ladies
9.	one _____	lots of copies
10.	one lorry	lots of _____

Challenge

Choose the correct plural to complete each sentence.

1. On the farm there were lots of _____. (gooses/geese)

2. I have two _____. (feet/foots)

3. Several _____ were shouting. (childs/children)

4. I had to have two _____ filled. (tooths/teeth)

5. There were some _____ in the field. (mouse/mice)

6. In the pond were several _____. (fish/fishes)

7. The fisherman caught some _____. (cod/cods)

8. We get wool from _____. (sheep/sheeps)

9. Two _____ were in the car. (mans/men)

10. The two _____ were talking. (womans/women)

Silent letters

Look and learn

Some words contain **silent letters**. We cannot hear them when we say the words.

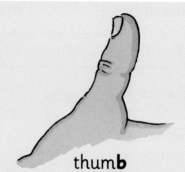

knot   thum**b**

Practice

comb	lamb	crumb	climb	thumb
knot	knee	knock	knife	knight

Use the correct word in each sentence. Circle the silent letter.

1. A knight was a soldier in olden times.   **2.** Your _____ is part of your hand.

3. A baby sheep is a _____.   **4.** You use a _____ to make your hair tidy.

5. We tie string together in a _____.   **6.** Your _____ is part of your leg.

7. A _____ is something you cut with.   **8.** A bird pecked at a _____ of bread.

9. You _____ a hill.   **10.** _____ means to strike or hit.

Challenge

Complete each of these words with a silent **g**, **w** or **l**.

1. ___rite   **2.** ___nat   **3.** ___reck

4. ___naw   **5.** ___rist   **6.** ta___k

7. ca___f   **8.** pa___m   **9.** ___nome

10. cha___k   **11.** ___nash   **12.** ___rap

13. ___rong   **14.** ___narled   **15.** ca___m

Adjectives

Look and learn

An **adjective** is a **describing** word. It tells us more about a **noun**.

a **loud** noise

a **rough** sea

Practice

Choose the best adjective to go with each noun.

old	funny	wide	small	sharp	open
tall	beautiful	ugly	fizzy	muddy	heavy

1. an _____open_____ door
2. a _____ river
3. a _____ drink
4. a _____ knife
5. a _____ clown
6. a _____ tree
7. a _____ kitten
8. an _____ monster
9. a _____ rock
10. a _____ puddle
11. a _____ princess
12. an _____ castle

Challenge

Match up the pairs of adjectives with similar meanings.

scared	hard
new	small
calm	sad
high	wet
wrong	fat
shut	sly

unhappy	tiny
crafty	closed
modern	damp
tall	frightened
plump	incorrect
difficult	still

Suffixes

Look and learn

A **suffix** is a group of letters we add to the **end** of a word.
A **suffix** changes the **meaning** of the word or changes the **job** the word does.

care + ful = careful

care + less = careless

Practice

Make the words.

| 1. use | ful | useful |
| | less | useless |

| 2. power | ful | ____ |
| | less | ____ |

| 3. help | ful | ____ |
| | less | ____ |

| 4. thought | ful | ____ |
| | less | ____ |

| 5. colour | ful | ____ |
| | less | ____ |

| 6. thank | ful | ____ |
| | less | ____ |

| 7. pain | ful | ____ |
| | less | ____ |

| 8. law | ful | ____ |
| | less | ____ |

| 9. hope | ful | ____ |
| | less | ____ |

| 10. care | ful | ____ |
| | less | ____ |

Challenge

Take the suffix off each word. Write the word you are left with.

1. beautiful _____beauty_____

2. wonderful _____

3. endless _____

4. speechless _____

5. plentiful _____

6. mindless _____

7. skilful _____

8. pitiless _____

9. dutiful _____

10. heartless _____

11. deceitful _____

12. merciless _____

Compound words

Look and learn

A **compound word** is a word made up of **two smaller words**.

horse   +   shoe   =   horseshoe

Practice

Do the word sums and make some compound words.

1. farm + yard = _____   **2.** bath + room = _____

3. pan + cake = _____   **4.** play + time = _____

5. sea + side = _____   **6.** tooth + brush = _____

7. sun + shine = _____   **8.** key + hole = _____

9. hand + bag = _____   **10.** sheep + dog = _____

11. grand + mother = _____   **12.** hand + writing = _____

Challenge

These pairs of compound words have got muddled. Write them correctly.

1.	runshake	handway		**2.**	snowcloth	tableball
	runway	handshake			_____	_____
3.	birthcard	postday		**4.**	wallbow	rainpaper
	_____	_____			_____	_____
5.	gentlenoon	afterman		**6.**	underpot	teaground
	_____	_____			_____	_____
7.	firepaste	toothwork		**8.**	eyeroom	cloaksight
	_____	_____			_____	_____
9.	midstep	footnight		**10.**	wallway	railpaper
	_____	_____			_____	_____

Subject and verb agreement

Look and learn

The **subject** (the main person or thing) and the **verb** in each sentence must agree.

The children is singing. ☒   The children are singing. ☑

Practice

Choose the correct form of the verb to complete each sentence.

1. Kangaroos _____ .   (jump/jumps)
2. A fish _____ .   (swim/swims)
3. The boy _____ .   (sing/sings)
4. The ladies _____ shopping.   (is/are)
5. The baby _____ crying.   (was/were)
6. She _____ hard.   (try/tries)
7. I _____ my homework.   (do/does)
8. They _____ to bed.   (go/goes)
9. The man _____ on Saturday.   (come/comes)
10. You _____ got it right.   (has/have)

Challenge

Rewrite these sentences in the plural. Make the necessary changes.

1. The girl has gone.   The girls have gone. _____
2. The man is singing. _____
3. The dog barks. _____
4. The child is smiling. _____
5. The owl was hunting. _____
6. The girl does well. _____
7. The clock ticks loudly. _____
8. The boy was skating. _____

Collective nouns

Look and learn

A **collective noun** is the name given to a **group** of things.

a **bunch** of grapes

a **flock** of sheep

Practice

Choose the best noun to complete each phrase.

stamps	cards	trees	sheep	soldiers	books
bees	crisps	cows	fish	bananas	ships

1. a herd of _____
2. a pack of _____
3. a swarm of _____
4. a flock of _____
5. a bunch of _____
6. a forest of _____
7. a collection of _____
8. a shoal of _____
9. a packet of _____
10. a library of _____
11. a fleet of _____
12. an army of _____

Challenge

Choose a suitable collective noun for each sentence.

1. Ben gave his mum a _____ of flowers.
2. Emma wore a _____ of beads round her neck.
3. An angry _____ of wasps buzzed around.
4. The man always carried a _____ of matches.
5. A _____ of birds flew past us.
6. In the forest there lived a _____ of wolves.
7. The _____ of singers sang beautifully.
8. There was a large _____ of spectators at the match.

Look and learn

We may **classify** adjectives according to **type**. These adjectives describe **shape**.

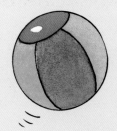

A **round** ball   a **square** cake   a **triangular** stamp

Practice

Sort these adjectives into the correct sets.

| small | red | oval | loud | huge | green |
| square | quiet | thin | blue | circular | squeaky |

colour adjectives	shape adjectives	size adjectives	sound adjectives
red			

Challenge

Fill in the missing letters to complete these adjectives about feelings.

1. | e | x | c | i | t | e | d |

2. | a | | | r | y |

3. | b | | | e | d |

4. | h | | | p | y |

5. | m | i | s | | | a | b | | |

6. | | | e | a | s | e | d |

7. | | | | o | y | e | d |

8. | j | | | | o | u | s |

9. | | | | s | e | t |

10. | | | | a | z | e | d |

Syllables

Look and learn

When we say a word slowly we can break it down into **smaller parts**.
These parts are called **syllables**. Each syllable must contain at least **one vowel**.

Be - ware   of   syl - lab - les!

(2 syllables)   (1 syllable)   (3 syllables)

Say words like a robot and hear the syllables.

Practice

Say these words slowly. Write if they have 1, 2 or 3 syllables in them.

1. come (_1_)

2. again (___)

3. robot (___)

4. tomorrow (___)

5. beginning (___)

6. when (___)

7. he (___)

8. maybe (___)

9. until (___)

10. this (___)

11. footballers (___)

12. musical (___)

13. hair (___)

14. today (___)

15. computer (___)

Challenge

Make some two-syllable words.

1.	rab	cil	_____
2.	pen	mer	_____
3.	win	on	_____
4.	drum	bit	_rabbit_
5.	bot	key	_____
6.	ro	dow	_____
7.	mon	bot	_____
8.	li	tle	_____

Look and learn

A **prefix** is a group of letters we put **in front** of a word.
Prefixes **change the meaning** of the word.

fill   refill

Practice

Choose the correct word to complete each sentence.

return	repay	replace	retake	replay
prefix	preheat	preface	precede	prepaid

1. I had to _____ the window I had broken.

2. A _____ is a group of letters we put in front of a word.

3. On Saturday I will _____ the books to the library.

4. _____ the milk before you add the custard powder.

5. The envelope was _____ so it did not need a stamp.

6. I had to _____ the free kick.

7. The game was called off so we will have to _____ it.

8. The author wrote a _____ at the beginning of the book.

9. _____ means to go in front of.

10. When you borrow money you have to _____ it.

Challenge

Choose the prefix **mis** or **ex** to complete each word.

1. __mis__ behave   **2.** _____ port   **3.** _____ judge

4. _____ pand   **5.** _____ handle   **6.** _____ calculate

7. _____ tract   **8.** _____ plode   **9.** _____ print

10. _____ understand   **11.** _____ use   **12.** _____ it

13. _____ cavate   **14.** _____ clude   **15.** _____ lead

Pronouns

Look and learn

A **pronoun** is a word that **takes the place** of a noun.

Amy ran for the bus, but Amy missed the bus.
Amy ran for the bus, but **she** missed **it**.

Practice

Choose the correct pronoun for each sentence.

1. The old man sat down. _____ was tired.   (She/He)
2. _____ am a good runner.   (I/we)
3. The children laughed as _____ played.   (it/they)
4. The girl cried when _____ hurt her ankle.   (she/he)
5. Ben and I are going out when _____ get home.   (you/we)
6. "Where are _____ going?" the man asked Siri.   (she/you)
7. The birds sang loudly when _____ woke up.   (they/you)
8. Where are my pens? Have you got _____?   (it/them)
9. I cleaned my bike when _____ got muddy.   (I/it)
10. The dog looked at the girl and barked at _____. (him/her)

Challenge

Say who or what each of the underlined pronouns stands for.

1. Sam caught the ball and threw <u>it</u> back.   _____the ball_____
2. Emma has two dogs. She takes <u>them</u> out every day.   _____
3. The baby played with her toy. It made <u>her</u> happy.   _____
4. The girl tried to ride her bike but she fell off <u>it</u>.   _____
5. The children ate sweets as <u>they</u> watched T.V.   _____
6. "Can <u>you</u> skip?" Ali asked Joel.   _____
7. "Come with <u>us</u>," Tom and Edward said to Shireen.   _____
8. "Fetch <u>me</u> my slippers, please," Mr Smith asked Sue.   _____
9. "<u>We</u> like chips," the twins said together.   _____
10. The robot looked around as <u>it</u> came through the door.   _____

Antonyms

Look and learn

Antonyms are words that have **opposite** meanings.

full   empty

Practice

Write the pairs of opposites.

| rough | cold | light | full | rich | expensive |
| old | loud | soft | wet | long | strong |

1. hot _____cold_____   **2.** weak _____   **3.** hard _____

4. dark _____   **5.** dry _____   **6.** empty _____

7. quiet _____   **8.** cheap _____   **9.** short _____

10. poor _____   **11.** smooth _____   **12.** young _____

Challenge

Circle the word in each set that is opposite to the word on the left.

1. rude	happy	wide	(polite)
2. noisy	quiet	heavy	tall
3. buy	walk	sell	climb
4. give	take	pour	drink
5. throw	lie	jump	catch
6. low	high	tiny	strong
7. wild	bad	tame	light
8. right	joyful	wrong	proud
9. come	go	hop	mix
10. stand	sneeze	eat	sit

1st and 3rd person

Look and learn

I played with Toby.
We had a good time.

Paul and Emma saw a monster.
It was horrible. **They** ran home.

| When we are writing about **ourselves** we write in the **1st person**. We use pronouns like **I** and **we**. | When we are writing about **others** we write in the **3rd person**. We use pronouns like **he**, **she**, **it** and **they**. |

Practice

Say whether each underlined pronoun is in the 1st person or 3rd person.

	1st person	3rd person
1. Edward went out when he was ready.		✓
2. I like eating crisps.		
3. Rob is my best friend. We always play together.		
4. The bear growled when it saw the man.		
5. The lady got out of the car when she had parked.		
6. The flowers looked lovely. They were colourful.		
7. I go to bed late every night.		
8. When Amy comes to my house we giggle a lot.		
9. The birds made a loud noise as they took off.		
10. The man tripped as he came down the stairs.		

Challenge

The sentences below are written in the 3rd person. Rewrite them in the 1st person.

Kira was walking through the wood when she saw something under a bush.
She bent down to have a look. She was surprised when she found it was a small box. Kira lifted the lid and looked inside. What a shock! Kira had found a diamond necklace. She wasn't sure what to do so she took it home and told her mother what she had discovered.

I was walking through the wood when I saw something under a bush.

Conjunctions

Look and learn

A **conjunction** is a **joining word**. It may be used to join **two sentences**.

I went home. I had my tea.

I went home **and** had my tea.

Practice

Rewrite these sentences. Use **and** or **but** to join them.

1. I went to the shop. I bought some sweets.

I went to the shop and I bought some sweets.

2. Abby is good at maths. She is a poor speller.

_____

3. An elephant is big. An ant is small.

_____

4. The dog saw me coming. It ran to me.

_____

5. Mrs Shah stopped the car. Her daughter got out.

_____

6. The lorry driver was slow. The police car was fast.

_____

Challenge

Finish each sentence in your own words. Underline the conjunction in each sentence.

1. You will hurt yourself if _____

2. I was late because _____

3. We will buy some sweets when _____

4. I tried to swim the river but _____

5. I went to the shop which _____

6. My hair was too long so _____

7. The toy has been broken since _____

8. I couldn't do it although _____

Look and learn

Spelling can be fun when you play with words!

lake

make **sh**ake **b**ake **qu**ake

turn train string

We can make words by **changing** letters.   We can make words by **adding** letters.

Practice

Make some new words.

1. Change the **f** in **f**ine to l, m, sh, wh: line   mine   shine   whine
2. Change the **c** in **c**are to b, d, fl, bew: _____
3. Change the **l** in **l**aw to p, r, s, cl: _____
4. Change the **p** in **p**ark to b, d, m, sh: _____
5. Change the **h** in **h**ound to f, p, gr, ar: _____
6. Change the **h** in **h**ead to d, dr, br, spr: _____
7. Change the **n** in **n**ice to r, sl, pr, tw: _____
8. Change the **w** in **w**age to c, p, st, vill: _____

Challenge

How many words can you make by adding letters?

Letters given	Some words you can make
blt	bolt, belt, ability
shd	
por	
cme	
mov	
wng	
fls	
ppg	

Possessive pronouns

Look and learn

Possessive pronouns tell us who the **owner** of something is.

> That's **my** pen. It's not **yours**. It's **mine**.

Some common possessive pronouns are:
my mine your yours his her hers its
our ours their theirs

Practice

Underline the possessive pronouns in these sentences.

1. This is <u>my</u> book. It is <u>mine</u>.
2. Sarah wore her new jeans and Nick wore his new trainers.
3. Our school is the best.
4. Emily and Andy looked for their bags.
5. We took our picnic in the car.
6. The ball had their name on it. It was theirs.
7. That is your car. It is yours.
8. I asked the girl if the book was hers.
9. This torch is mine.
10. The dragon opened its mouth wide.

Challenge

Think of a suitable possessive pronoun for each gap.

1. Do these shoes belong to you? Are they _____?
2. The ball belongs to those children. It is _____.
3. Ian took _____ dog for a walk.
4. Sita spilt drink down _____ dress.
5. We tried hard to finish _____ picture first.
6. The car had a dent in _____ bonnet.
7. The girls picked up _____ magazines and read them.
8. The lady was sure the hat was _____.

Apostrophes

Look and learn

Sometimes we **shorten** words and **leave letters out**. These words are called **contractions**. We use an **apostrophe** to show where letters are missing.

Don't do that!

Do not → Don't

Practice

Match each contraction with its longer form.

isn't	wasn't	doesn't	she's	it's	wouldn't
you're	I've	we'll	I'm	we'd	won't

1. she is ____she's____

2. you are _____

3. does not _____

4. I have _____

5. is not _____

6. we would _____

7. was not _____

8. we will _____

9. would not _____

10. will not _____

11. it is _____

12. I am _____

Challenge

Put in the missing apostrophes in the correct places.

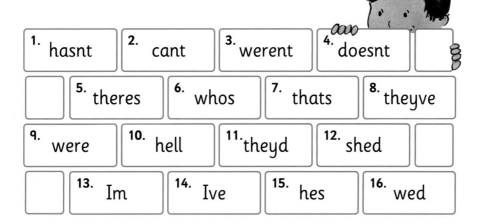

1. hasnt 2. cant 3. werent 4. doesnt

5. theres 6. whos 7. thats 8. theyve

9. were 10. hell 11. theyd 12. shed

13. Im 14. Ive 15. hes 16. wed

More speech marks

Look and learn

When we write down what people say we use **speech marks**.
The **words a person says** go **inside** the speech marks.

Are you coming out to play?

No, I have to go to bed early.

"Are you coming out to play?" Sarah asked.

Liz replied, "No, I have to go to bed early."

Practice

Fill in the missing speech marks in each sentence.

1. "Stop! shouted the boy.
2. May I come?" Tom asked.
3. "My dress is muddy, said the girl.
4. Ian whispered, "I'm fed up.
5. The lady asked, Where is my bag?"
6. It's nearly tea time," the man said.
7. "Pass the salt, please, asked Mr Shah.
8. Carl shouted, Run for it!"

Challenge

Decide if there are any missing speech marks. If there are put them in.

	Yes	No
1. Why are you late? the man asked.	✓	
2. Emma said, These sums are hard.		
3. The plane took off from Heathrow Airport.		
4. The grass needs mowing again, moaned Mr Burns.		
5. The lightning struck the tall oak tree.		
6. In autumn, leaves fall off the trees.		
7. Please don't shout, the teacher urged.		
8. These are my favourite crisps! Paula exclaimed.		

Look and learn

A **proper noun** is the **special** (or **particular**) name of a **person**, **place** or **thing**. Proper nouns always begin with a **capital letter**.

This is **M**arie.

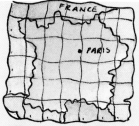

Paris is in **F**rance.

This is the **E**iffel **T**ower.

Practice

Rewrite these proper nouns. Begin each one with a capital letter.

1. snow white   _Snow White_

2. march   _____

3. cardiff   _____

4. king street   _____

5. hyde park   _____

6. london bridge   _____

7. humpty dumpty   _____

8. the daily herald   _____

9. radio times   _____

10. manchester united   _____

11. river seine   _____

12. tuesday   _____

13. grand hotel   _____

14. dr smith   _____

Challenge

Remember the capital letters. Write the names of four:

1. months containing 31 days   _____
2. countries beginning with B   _____
3. famous people   _____
4. towns near you   _____
5. mountains   _____
6. pop groups   _____
7. newspapers or magazines   _____
8. good friends   _____

Answers

Page 2
Practice: 2. unfair, 3. undress, 4. unwell, 5. unpack, 6. distrust, 7. disobey, 8. dishonest, 9. disarm, 10. displace
Challenge: 1. b) disobey, c) unfair, d) undress, e) distrust, f) dishonest, g) undo, h) disarm, i) displace, j) unwell
2. a) unbolt, b) disown, c) discharge, d) unbuckle, e) dismay, f) disorder, g) unfasten, h) unwrap, i) unable or disable

Page 3
Practice: 2. dived, 3. roared, 4. knocked, 5. broke, 6. bit, 7. painted, 8. fell, 9. shone, 10. took
Challenge: push/shove, vanish/disappear, run/race, close/shut, brush/sweep, moan/groan, speak/talk, drink/swallow, draw/sketch, bang/hit

Page 4
Practice: 2. now, 3. pay, 4. barn, 5. goat, 6. pain, 7. again, 8. paw, 9. sauce, 10. raw
Challenge: 2. pool, 3. roast, 4. paint, 5. crown, 6. crayon, 7. about, 8. spoil, 9. beast, 10. blue, 11. grow, 12. burn

Page 5
Practice:
ble words: cable, table, stumble
dle words: handle, needle, cradle
ple words: people, simple, steeple
kle words: ankle, sparkle, twinkle
Challenge: 2. uncle, 3. circle, 4. eagle, 5. single, 6. ankle, 7. bubble, 8. dazzle, 9. nibble, 10. cattle

Page 6
Practice:
1. What colour is grass?
2. We have got curry for dinner.
3. My pencil is blunt.
4. Where have you put my glasses?
5. When is your birthday?
6. The clock is broken.
Challenge:
2. This is awful! (E)
3. Help, I'm drowning! (E)
4. Have you seen Sita? (Q)
5. Who is the winner? (Q)
6. Are you lost? (Q)
7. Don't shout! (E)
8. When are you leaving? (Q)
9. How much does it cost? (Q)
10. Look out! (E)
11. Run for it! (E)
12. What time is it? (Q)

Page 7
Practice:
1. "What would you like to eat?" Mrs Jones asked.
2. "I would like a sandwich, please," Tom replied.
3. "What would you like in it?" Mrs Jones asked.
4. "Cheese and pickle, please," Tom answered.
5. "I'll go and make it," Mrs Jones told Tom.
6. "Shall I make us a cup of tea?" Tom asked.
7. "That would be nice," Mrs Jones replied.
8. "Afterwards I'll watch TV," Tom added.
Challenge: answers may vary

Page 8
Practice:
1. duck, fish, goat
2. roof, stall, teapot
3. lolly, milk, onion
4. ambulance, car, lorry
5. fall, fly, fog, frog
6. shine, skin, slip, spleen
Challenge: answers may vary

Page 9
Practice: 2. walk/walked, 3. carry/carried, 4. tug/tugged, 5. catch/caught, 6. see/saw, 7. write/wrote, 8. come/came, 9. feel/felt, 10. go/went
Challenge: 1. bit, 2. hurt, 3. broke, 4. caught, 5. flew, 6. shook, 7. bought, 8. built, 9. saw, 10. grew

Page 10
Practice:
1. On the table were some potatoes, carrots, a cabbage and peas.
2. My favourite colours are red, yellow, blue and green.
3. In my bag I had some pens, pencils, crayons and a ruler.
4. Curry, pizza, burgers and sausages are my favourite foods.
5. The four seasons are summer, autumn, winter and spring.
6. The four pets I have are a dog, a cat, a gerbil and a mouse.
7. I collect stamps, coins, badges and shells.
8. History, art, maths and science are good subjects.
Challenge: answers may vary

Page 11
Practice: 2. man/any/an, 3. so/me, 4. eve/ever/very, 5. he/here, 6. hear/ear/he, 7. be/for/or/ore, 8. me/age/sage/mess, 9. hall/shall/low/allow/all, 10. car/care/scar (answers may vary)
Challenge: 2. fed, 3. my, 4. cap, 5. price, 6. swing, 7. fat, 8. sting, 9. show, 10. car

Page 12
Practice:
2. A plumber mends burst water pipes.
3. A clown makes us laugh.
4. A church is a place where people worship.
5. A farm is a place where crops can be grown.
6. A shop is a place where we buy things.
7. A fence is used to separate two pieces of land.
8. A spade is used to dig holes.
9. An envelope is used to put letters in.
10. A saucepan is used to cook food in.
Challenge:
2. shoe – All the others are fruit.
3. trumpet – All the others are vegetables.
4. pencil – All the others are furniture.
5. book – All the others are cutlery.
6. bear – All the others are jobs people do.
7. ball – All the others are musical instruments.
8. window – All the others are tools.

Page 13
Practice: 1. cars, 2. book, 3. brushes, 4. bus, 5. dishes, 6. foxes, 7. babies, 8. lady, 9. copy, 10. lorries
Challenge: 1. geese, 2. feet, 3. children, 4. teeth, 5. mice, 6. fish, 7. cod, 8. sheep, 9. men, 10. women

Page 14
Practice: 2. thumb, 3. lamb, 4. comb, 5. knot, 6. knee, 7. knife, 8. crumb, 9. climb, 10. knock
Challenge: 1. write, 2. gnat, 3. wreck, 4. gnaw, 5. wrist, 6. talk, 7. calf, 8. palm, 9. gnome, 10. chalk, 11. gnash, 12. wrap, 13. wrong, 14. gnarled, 15. calm

Page 15
Practice: 2. wide, 3. fizzy, 4. sharp, 5. funny, 6. tall, 7. small, 8. ugly, 9. heavy, 10. muddy, 11. beautiful, 12. old
Challenge: hard/difficult, new/modern, small/tiny, calm/still, sad/unhappy, high/tall, wet/damp, wrong/incorrect, fat/plump, shut/closed, sly/crafty

Page 16
Practice: 2. powerful/powerless, 3. helpful/helpless, 4. thoughtful/thoughtless, 5. colourful/colourless, 6. thankful/thankless, 7. painful/painless, 8. lawful/lawless, 9. hopeful/hopeless, 10. careful/careless
Challenge: 2. wonder, 3. end, 4. speech, 5. plenty, 6. mind, 7. skill, 8. pity, 9. duty, 10. heart, 11. deceit, 12. mercy